The GAMB LS

BOOK Nº 38

by Bar... by

£ 2·00

HERE WE GO AGAIN — FOR THE 38TH TIME — YES THIS IS BOOK
NUMBER 38 — ANOTHER RECORD OF OUR ADVENTURES
OVER THE PAST YEAR

# THE YEAR STARTED PRETTY MUCH THE SAME AS ANY OTHER YEAR

THERE WERE THE BILLS TO PAY

AND THE SHOPPING

THERE WAS THE LAUNDRY TO SEE TO— THE TENNIS TO WATCH AND THE NEVER ENDING TASK OF KEEPING UP WITH FASHION

AH GOOD — YOU FOUND IT — ER.. YES — YOU CAN PUT IT BACK NOW

TWO HOURS SEARCHING FOR IT AND ONE **SECOND** LOOKING AT IT — OOH!!

©1988 Barry Appleby    4300

THE FIGURES FOR THE FIRST...

... AND I HAVE TO RECORD..

AND NOW FOR THE **LESS** INTERESTING PART OF MY REPORT......

© 1988 Barry Appleby    4294

IN THE TIME LEFT OVER FROM ALL THESE
PURSUITS WE RE-DECORATED THE HOUSE
FROM TOP TO BOTTOM

THERE WAS THE NEVER TO BE FORGOTTEN DAY
WHEN GEORGE DECIDED TO GROW A BEARD

A GREAT DEAL OF GEORGE'S SPARE TIME
WAS OCCUPIED WITH HIS NEVER ENDING
WORK ON RESTORING HIS OLD CAR

COME TO THINK OF IT— DURING THE PAST YEAR
WE HAVE HAD MORE ILLNESS THAN USUAL— IT
STARTED WITH GAYE CATCHING A COLD

DARLING — YOU ARE **WONDERFUL**

YOU MUST BE THE ONLY MAN IN THE WHOLE WORLD WHO CAN <u>BURN</u> A TIN OF SOUP

©1988 Barry Appleby 4336

BLAST! — THERE AREN'T ANY CLEAN CUPS, SAUCERS OR PLATES

AH WELL

©1988 Barry Appleby

CAR WASH

4337

AND AS HAPPENS IN ALL FAMILIES GAYE PASSED HER COLD ON TO GEORGE

4340

4341

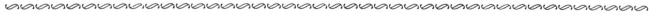

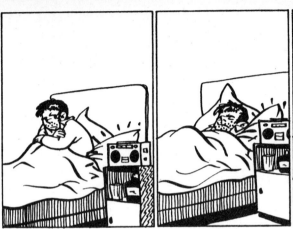

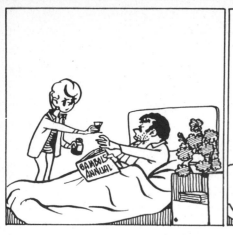

NO SOONER HAD WE RECOVERED FROM OUR COLDS
THAN NIECE MIGGY AND NEPHEW FLIVVER CAME TO STAY

AND JUST AS THE CHILDREN WERE ABOUT TO
GO BACK TO SCHOOL THAN THEY CAUGHT
MEASLES AND GAYE CAUGHT IT FROM THEM

AND OF COURSE
WE MUSTN'T
FORGET GEORGE'S
ATTEMPT AT
THE MARATHON

23-4

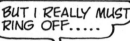

AS IN EVERY YEAR ONE OF THE HIGHLIGHTS WAS
OUR ANNUAL HOLIDAY IN THE SUN SHINE

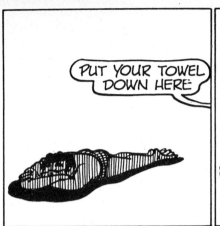

IT SEEMED NO TIME AT ALL AFTER WE HAD RETURNED
FROM OUR HOLIDAYS THAN IT WAS CHRISTMAS

AND THAT'S WHAT HAPPENED TO US DURING THE PAST YEAR—NOW WE GO OFF TO START SOME NEW CARTOONS — WE HOPE TO SEE YOU EVERY DAY IN THE DAILY EXPRESS AND THE SUNDAY EXPRESS

©1989 *Barry Appleby*

Published by Express Newspapers plc, Fleet Street, London EC4P 4JT, and printed by Grosvenor Press (Portsmouth) Ltd.